Usborne
Mermaids
Sticker Book

Illustrated by Camilla Garofano

Designed by Mary Cartwright
& Nancy Leschnikoff

Written by Fiona Watt

At the back of this book, you will find lots of stickers.
Some of them are especially sparkly - can you find them?

Contents

On the rocks

Waves splash gently against the seaweed-covered rocks as a group of mermaids sit combing their hair, while others swim in the shallow water. Friendly seabirds perch on the rocks beside them.

Seashell grotto

Deep underwater, mermaids are decorating a secret grotto. The walls and columns are covered with mosaics made from hundreds of shells and pieces of smooth glass that they've gathered from the shoreline.

Playing with dolphins

When a brisk wind whips up the surface of the sea mermaids and dolphins love to play. They dive and swim together through the foamy waves.

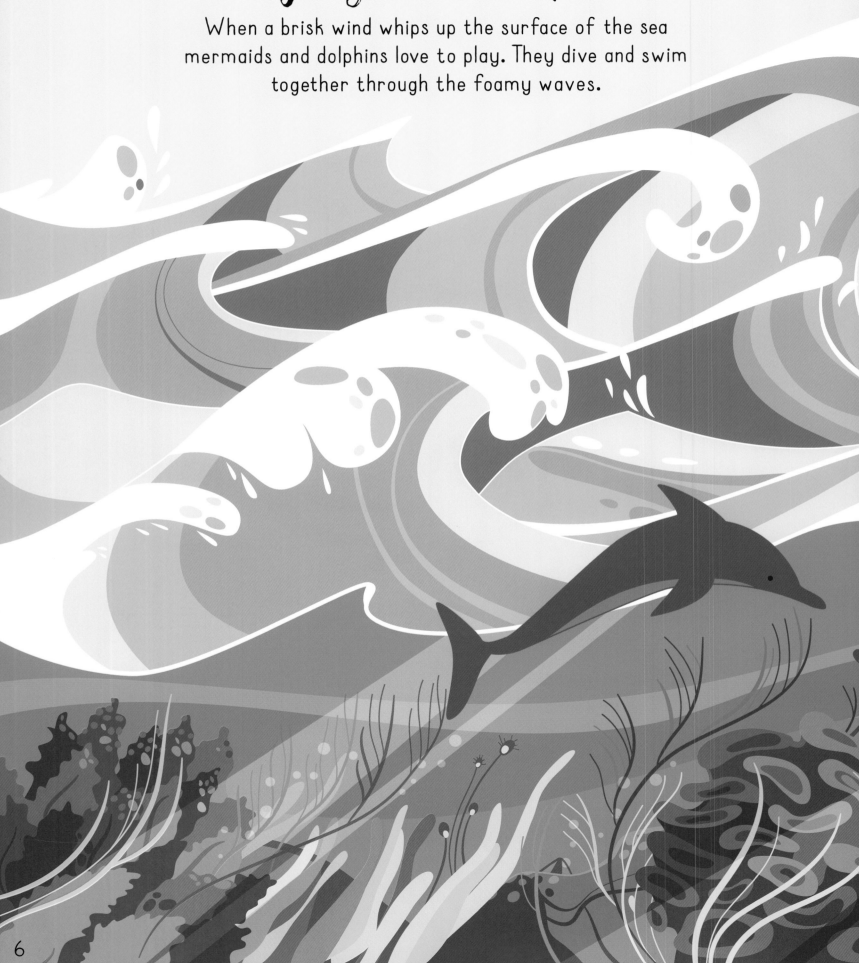

Deep Sea Spa

Warm water, heated by underground volcanoes, bubbles through chimney-like vents in the seafloor. Mermaids have gathered to relax, chat, be pampered and have their hair styled.

Getting ready

Oriana, Marika, Maya and Lana are getting ready
to go to a party. They've adorned themselves
with beads and bangles, and added
accessories to their hair.

Oriana

Marika

Maya

Lana

11

Crystal cave

Crystals glisten in the shadowy light that filters down into an ice cave. Over the years, mermaids have carved pictures of fish and mysterious sea creatures into the floor and walls.

Mermaid queen

Seated on a splendid seashell throne, Queen Sirena is celebrating her birthday. Every year, mermaids from her undersea kingdom present her with rare sparkly shells, while exotic fish and jellyfish swim around.

Musical mermaids

In a ruined underwater city, a group of mermaids blow gently into seashells, while others sing sweetly. Far above them, sailors sailing by are entranced by the enchanting music and wonder where it's coming from.

Seashell carriages

Mermaids, tired of swimming, sometimes climb into carriages made from giant seashells. Elegant seahorses pull them through the water, while other seahorses and little fish swim beside them.

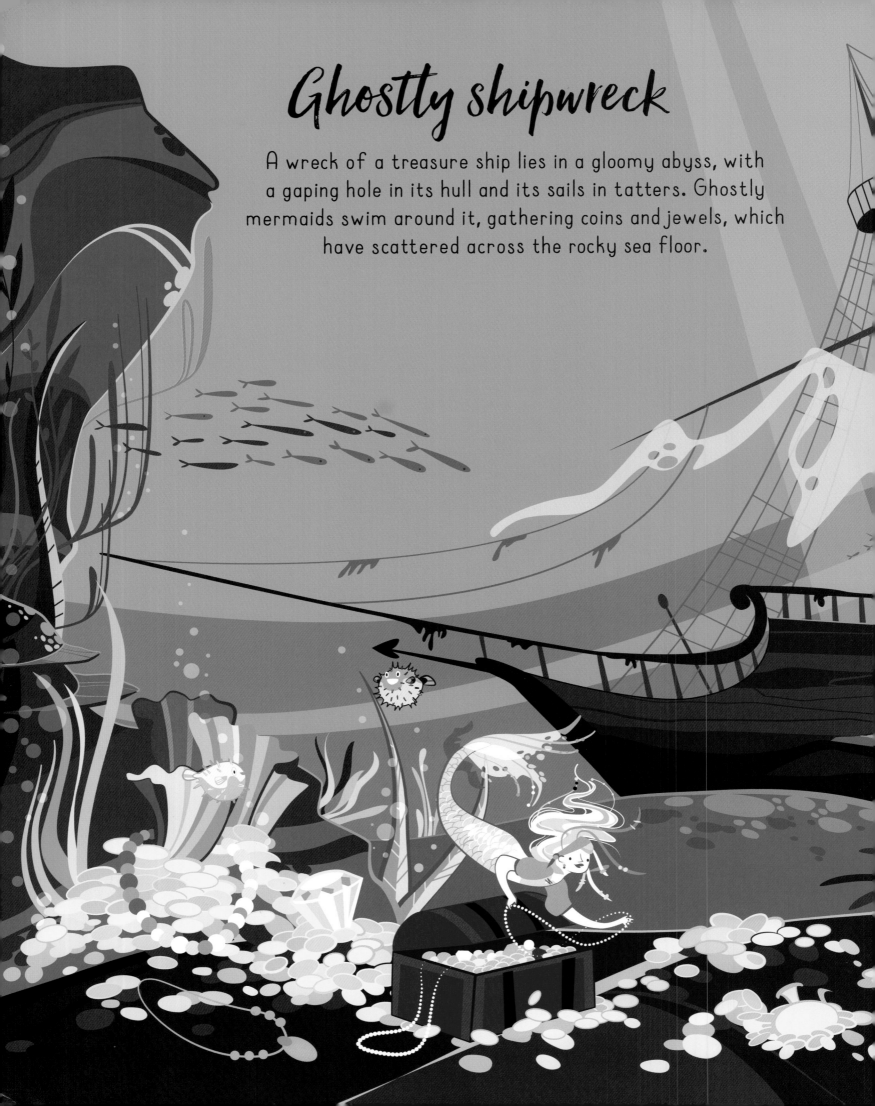

Ghostly shipwreck

A wreck of a treasure ship lies in a gloomy abyss, with a gaping hole in its hull and its sails in tatters. Ghostly mermaids swim around it, gathering coins and jewels, which have scattered across the rocky sea floor.

Sea otters

As sunlight filters through a cool kelp forest, hungry sea otters search for spiky sea urchins to eat. Mermaids gather to watch them as they tumble and dive amongst the towering fronds of seaweed.

Matching mermaids

Match the mermaid stickers from the last sticker page to these shapes.

Luna

Moonflower

Marina

Marissa

Ayumi

Calypso

Delfina

Nerissa

Avalon

Crystal

Galia

First published in 2018 by Usborne Publishing Ltd., 83-85 Saffron Hill, London, EC1N 8RT, England. www.usborne.com
Copyright © 2018 Usborne Publishing Ltd. The name Usborne and the devices ♈ ⊕ are Trade Marks of Usborne Publishing Ltd.

On the rocks
Pages 2-3

Seashell grotto
Pages 4-5

More stickers for the grotto
Pages 4-5

Playing with dolphins
Pages 6-7

Deep sea spa
Pages 8-9

Getting ready
Pages 10-11

Oriana's hair accessory

Oriana's
necklace

This goes around
her tail.

Maya's hair
accessories

For Maya's tail

A necklace

Bangles

Hang these on
the coral.

For Marika's hair

Bangles

For Marika's
tail

Crystal cave   Pages 12-13

Mermaid queen
Pages 14-15

Musical mermaids   Pages 16-17

Seashell carriages
Pages 18-19

More seashell carriages
Pages 18-19

Ghostly shipwreck
Pages 20-21

Extra stickers for any picture